RISING ★ STARS

Rising Stars UK Ltd.
22 Grafton Street, London W1S 4EX
www.risingstars-uk.com

nasen

NASEN House, 4/5 Amber Business Village, Amber Close,
Amington, Tamworth, Staffordshire B77 4RP

Text © Rising Stars UK Ltd.
The right of Paul Blum to be identified as the author of this work has
been asserted by him in accordance with the Copyright, Design and
Patents Act 1988.

Published 2008

Cover design: pentacorbig
Illustrator: Chris King, Illustration Ltd.
Text design and typesetting: pentacorbig
Publisher: Gill Budgell
Editor: Catherine Baker
Editorial project management: Margot O'Keeffe
Editorial consultant: Lorraine Petersen
Photos: Alamy, Sam Ralli

British Library Cataloguing in Publication Data.
A CIP record for this book is available from the British Library.

ISBN: 978-1-84680-458-8

Printed by Craft Print International Limited, Singapore

shadows

Contents

The Crash

- The Crash happened in 2021. Alien space ships crash landed on Earth.

- After The Crash, the Earth became very cold and dark.

- Now the aliens rule the world.

- The aliens have changed shape so they look like people.

- People call the aliens The Enemy.

Life after the Crash

- People are afraid.

- They do not know who is an Enemy and who is a friend.

The Firm

- The Firm keeps order on the streets.

- The Firm keeps people safe from Enemy attacks.

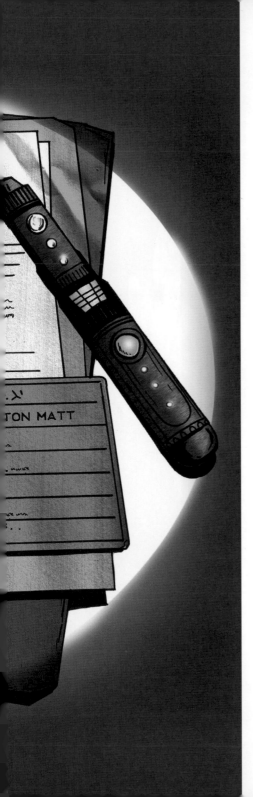

About Matt Merton

Matt Merton works for The Firm. He often works with Dexter. Their job is to find and kill The Enemy. They use Truth Sticks to do this.

But Matt has problems.

Matt has lost his memory. He cannot answer some big questions.

- Where has Jane, his girlfriend, gone?

- How did he get his job with The Firm?

Matt thinks The Firm is on the side of good. But is it?

chapter 1

Matt Merton sat in the bar.

Matt liked to sit in the shadows. In the shadows, Matt could think.

Sam, the bar man, came over.

'Do you want another drink?' he said.

'No thanks,' said Matt. 'I've got to go. I've got work to do.'

Matt had a tip-off. The Enemy were planning something.

They were planning to bomb the city.

chapter 2

Matt had to go to the airport. He knew what his target looked like now.

He had to stop him.

Matt took the sky tram. He looked out of the window.

It was a grey day. It was raining. Always winter and never summer since The Crash.

Matt went into the airport.

He looked at all the people. He looked deep into
their eyes.

Then Matt saw him. He had 'the look' of The Enemy ...

… But he had a woman and a child with him.

Matt had to be sure. He did not want to hurt the woman and child.

He had to be sure he had got the right man.

chapter 3

Matt began to ask the man questions.

'What is your name?' he said.

The man looked away.

'What is your mother's name?' Matt said.

The man tried to run. He tried to drag the woman and child with him.

But Matt was too fast.

He took out the Truth Stick.

'I work for The Firm. You are under arrest,'
Matt shouted.

He shone the Truth Stick into the man's eyes.

'No!' shouted the man. 'My wife! My little girl!'

Matt stopped. He could not do it. He felt sorry for the man. He felt sorry for his family.

The man started to run.

chapter 4

Matt heard a voice behind him.

'Stop right now. It's The Firm!' said the voice.
It was Dexter.

Dexter took out his Truth Stick. He shone it into the man's eyes.

The man died.

Matt stood still. Dexter pointed his finger in Matt's face.

'What is wrong with you, Merton? I saw what you did.
I saw it all.'

Matt said nothing.

'You're no good to The Firm,' said Dexter. 'You're no good to anyone. You've lost your nerve.'

Dexter walked off. Matt did not follow him.

Matt took the sky tram home. There was a lot to think about.

For Dexter, killing The Enemy was easy. Being in The Firm was easy.

But for Matt, it was hard. Too hard.

about the author

AUTHOR NAME
Paul Blum

JOB
Teacher

LAST KNOWN LOCATION
North London, England

NOTES
Before The Crash taught in Inner–city London
schools. Writer of series of books called
The Extraordinary Files. Believed to be in
hiding from The Firm. Wanted for questioning.
Seems to know more about The Enemy than
he should ...